Book of James Volume 1

Developing
A Faith
That Works

Taught by Pastor Rick Warren

Published by Purpose Driven® Publishing
Saddleback Church
1 Saddleback Parkway
Lake Forest, CA 92630
www.purposedriven.com

TABLE OF CONTENTS

You have just opened up a power tool. It doesn't look like a tool, it doesn't feel like a tool, and it doesn't have a power cord, but it's definitely a tool! This tool was designed for you, an ordinary Christian—the kind of Christian who sincerely desires to live for God and yet struggles to stay on track. If you are the kind of Christian whose life is fast-paced and full but not always fulfilled, this tool is for you.

This curriculum tool is like any tool: it needs to be used. Put this tool into action and it will be productive in your life and in your group. The Purpose Driven Bible Study Series may have a few features that are new to you, but we encourage you to give them a try. A tool is most effective when used for its intended purpose. This curriculum tool has three intended purposes.

1. Digging Deeper Into the Word of God

Each of the six lessons in this curriculum includes study of at least one core biblical passage. This interactive study not only allows for discussion of the passage, but also provides opportunity to discuss practical application as a response to the passage. Tremendous spiritual power is experienced when a group wrestles with not only the meaning of a passage but also its meaning for their lives.

2. Building Community

No Christ-follower was intended to live in isolation. The Bible speaks nothing of "lone ranger" faith, but more than fifty times in the New Testament, God speaks of a "one another" type of faith. One of the great benefits of group life is that it provides you with a practical laboratory in which to experience New Testament community. In group life you find a place to belong and people with whom to share your life.

3. Sharpening Your Focus on God's Purposes

One unique feature of this tool is that it seeks to balance all five purposes of God in your group experience. Without an intentional focus on including all five purposes, most groups focus on fellowship or become a Bible study group only. This study is designed to help create and nurture a hunger and passion to live out all of God's purposes for his children.

So, pick it up. Don't be afraid of it. Use it. Allow it to stretch and challenge you. God has put your group together and wants to use each member in your life. He wants to use you in their lives as well. So pray for your group and come to your group time ready to participate. May you build a life that is pleasing to God.

Outline of Each Session

You are about to embark on a life-changing experience in your small group. Studying God's Word together with other believers always impacts our lives in ways we can't imagine.

As your group studies the Bible together, this study guide will help you strengthen and deepen God's five purposes for your lives. One of the unique features of this curriculum is that it uses the five purposes as the format for each session. When you see the following symbols and elements in the study guide, you will know the particular purpose that section promotes. The format of each session is as follows:

 Connect (Fellowship) — Intimate connection with God and his family is the foundation for spiritual growth. The questions in this section will help you get to know the members of your group so you'll begin to feel a sense of belonging and family.

 Grow (Discipleship) — Each week you will watch Pastor Rick Warren's teaching video for the session. We ask you to follow along using the teaching outline in your study guide and your Bibles. After the teaching video, discuss the questions that follow. The questions are designed to facilitate a deeper understanding of the Bible and help you consider how the truths of the Bible can impact your life.

 Serve (Ministry) — Nothing is more fulfilling than using your God-given gifts to serve and help meet the needs of others in God's family. This section will help make that desire a reality. You will be encouraged to discover your unique shape and challenged to take steps to serve those inside and outside your group.

 Share (Evangelism) — The thought of sharing your faith can be scary and relationally awkward. Such feelings are common and understandable. But God can and wants to use you to reach those around you for Christ. The Share section is designed to give you and your group practical, manageable steps for sharing Christ that can become a part of your everyday life.

 Worship — In each small group session you will have the opportunity to surrender your heart to God and express your worship to him. You will be introduced in this section to various forms of small group worship including prayer, singing together, and sharing what God is doing in your lives. This portion of your session can be very meaningful for your group. If singing and praying in a group is new to you, feel free to not participate until you feel comfortable.

Additional Study — If your group wants a little more Bible study and has the time, we provide a few additional questions to discuss. This is optional.

Preparation for Next Week —This section is for groups or individuals willing to do more study during the week. You could use these questions to go deeper biblically, reflect on the lesson, or record your thoughts in a journal. This section generally includes cross-references relevant to the subject you will study the coming week. It will also include questions and practical ideas for applying the upcoming week's lesson.

Memory Verse — In each session we provide a verse to memorize. While this may be a challenge for you, please take this opportunity to grow deeper in your walk with God in this key spiritual habit.

Host Tips — We have provided a number of questions in each section of the curriculum. As the host we encourage you to select the questions you believe are most beneficial for your group. If your group is unable to work through the entire curriculum, we have recommended a question or activity with an asterisk (*) in each section of the study. These brief instructions in gray type are helpful coaching hints for your group host. Here's your first tip . . .

HOST TIP: THE STUDY GUIDE MATERIAL IS MEANT TO BE YOUR SERVANT, NOT YOUR MASTER. SO PLEASE DON'T FEEL YOU HAVE TO ANSWER EVERY QUESTION IN EVERY SECTION. THE POINT IS NOT TO RACE THROUGH THE SESSION; THE POINT IS TO TAKE TIME TO LET GOD WORK IN YOUR LIVES. NOR IS IT NECESSARY TO "GO AROUND THE CIRCLE" BEFORE YOU MOVE ON TO THE NEXT QUESTION. GIVE PEOPLE THE FREEDOM TO SPEAK, BUT DON'T INSIST THAT THEY DO. YOUR GROUP WILL ENJOY DEEPER, MORE OPEN SHARING AND DISCUSSION IF PEOPLE DON'T FEEL PRESSURED TO SPEAK UP. IF YOUR GROUP IS UNABLE TO WORK THROUGH ALL THE MATERIAL IN A SESSION, WE HAVE RECOMMENDED ONE QUESTION OR ACTIVITY WITH AN ASTERISK (*) IN EACH SECTION OF THE STUDY.

HOW TO USE THIS VIDEO CURRICULUM

Follow these simple steps for a successful small group session:

1. Open your group meeting by using the Connect section in your study guide.

2. Watch Pastor Rick's video teaching and follow along in the outlines in the study guide. Each video lesson is about twenty minutes in length.

3. Complete the rest of the discussion materials for each session in the study guide.

It's just that simple. Have a great study together!

1

SESSION ONE:
HOW TO PROFIT
FROM YOUR PROBLEMS

JAMES 1:1–6

Connect . . . . .15 minutes

> HOST TIP: IF YOUR GROUP IS UNABLE TO WORK THROUGH THE ENTIRE SESSION, WE HAVE RECOMMENDED ONE QUESTION
> OR ACTIVITY (INDICATED WITH AN ASTERISK [*]) IN EACH SECTION OF THE STUDY.

1. How did you come to be a part of this group? *I was invited by Stacy Harris, my friend*

*2. What are one or two things you hope to gain from participating in this small group? Do you want to develop new relationships, deepen your faith in God, learn about how to study the Bible, be encouraged in your Christian walk, or something else? *To live my life more aware of Christ in all I do.*

3. Open to the *Purpose Driven Group Guidelines* in the *Small Group Resources* section of the study guide, page 66. Take a few minutes to review these group guidelines before you begin this first of a two-part series on the book of James. These guidelines will help everyone know what to expect from the group and how to contribute to a worthwhile study.

Grow . . . . .35–40 minutes

Memory Verse

*Consider it pure joy, my brothers, whenever you face trials of many kinds,
because you know that the testing of your faith develops perseverance.*
James 1:2–3 (NIV)

Watch the video now. Follow along in your Bibles and take notes on the outline.

¹James, a servant of God and of the Lord Jesus Christ, to the twelve tribes scattered among the nations: Greetings. ²Consider it pure joy, my brothers, whenever you face trials of many kinds, ³because you know that the testing of your faith develops perseverance. ⁴Perseverance must finish its work so that you may be mature and complete, not lacking anything. ⁵If any of you lacks wisdom, he should ask God, who gives generously to all without finding fault, and it will be given to him. ⁶But when he asks, he must believe and not doubt, because he who doubts is like a wave of the sea, blown and tossed by the wind. (James 1:1–6 NIV)

Four Facts of Life You Need to Know

²Consider it pure joy, my brothers, whenever you face trials of many kinds, ³because you know that the testing of your faith develops perseverance. (James 1:2–3 NIV)

1. Problems are *a test of faith* *inevitable*
2. Problems are *opportunities to grow* *unpredictable*
3. Problems are *variable* .
4. Problems are *purposeful* .

Three Values of Problems

³ᵇThe testing of your faith develops perseverance, ⁴. . . so that you may be mature and complete, not lacking anything. (James 1:3b–4 NIV)

1. Problems purify my *true heart faith* .
2. Problems fortify my *patience* .
3. Problems sanctify my *Character* .

God's Ultimate Purpose in my life: Building the *Character* into my life.

How to Handle Your Problems

1. _Rejoice_

   We don't rejoice _for_ the problem, but we

   rejoice _in_ the problem.

   In everything give thanks; for this is God's will for you in Christ Jesus.
   (1 Thessalonians 5:18 NASB)

2. _Pray_

   If any of you lacks wisdom, he should ask God, who gives generously to all without
   finding fault, and it will be given to him. (James 1:5 NIV) _what do you_
   want me to learn

   Pray for _wisdom_

3. _Relax_

   But when he asks, he must believe and not doubt . . ." (James 1:6a NIV)

Discussion Questions

1. Why does James tell us to *"consider it pure joy"* when we encounter problems?
   What does James say will result from these trials in life (verses 3–4)?

*2. James urges three godly responses to problems: Rejoice, pray, and relax. Which of
   these responses is the most difficult for you when you are facing a problem? Why?

3 Most of the time we don't understand why problems come our way or what their
   purpose could be. What does James tell us to do in verse 5? Why is this good
   advice when we find ourselves in circumstances that don't make sense to us?

HOST TIP: ADDITIONAL QUESTIONS ARE PROVIDED AT THE END OF THIS LESSON FOR YOUR GROUP TO STUDY. DEPENDING ON THE SIZE OF YOUR GROUP, THE LENGTH OF TIME YOU'RE MEETING TOGETHER, AND/OR THE MEMBERS' LEVEL OF CHRISTIAN MATURITY, YOU MAY WANT TO USE THESE QUESTIONS AS SUGGESTED HOMEWORK EACH WEEK OR TURN THERE NOW FOR EXTENDED DISCUSSION.

Serve . . . . .15 minutes

³Praise be to the God and Father of our Lord Jesus Christ, the Father of compassion and the God of all comfort, ⁴who comforts us in all our troubles, so that we can comfort those in any trouble with the comfort we ourselves have received from God. ⁵For just as the sufferings of Christ flow over into our lives, so also through Christ our comfort overflows. ⁶If we are distressed, it is for your comfort and salvation; if we are comforted, it is for your comfort, which produces in you patient endurance of the same sufferings we suffer. ⁷And our hope for you is firm, because we know that just as you share in our sufferings, so also you share in our comfort. (2 Corinthians 1:3–7 NIV)

1. According to this passage, what will the difficulties of life prepare you to do in service to others?

*2. 2 Corinthians 1:3–7 tells us how God uses suffering in our life so that we can help others in times of trouble. What are some specific ways God has comforted you in your times of suffering? Which of these experiences has helped you comfort others in their times of need?

Share . . . . .10 minutes

Problems often provide us with opportunities to purify our faith, fortify our patience, and sanctify our character. As we see God's work in our lives, we naturally desire to share with others what God has done for us.

1. In what ways can a life that has "profited from problems" open doors for sharing Christ with those around us?

*2. Turn to the *Circles of Life* on page 68 in the *Small Group Resources* section. Use this tool to help you identify those around you who need to know Jesus. Make a plan to invite them to join you the next time this group meets. Ask the group to pray for them this week.

Worship . . . . .20 minutes

HOST TIP: To MAXIMIZE PRAYER TIME AND ALLOW GREATER OPPORTUNITY FOR PERSONAL SHARING, BREAK INTO SUBGROUPS OF THREE OR FOUR PEOPLE. THIS IS ESPECIALLY IMPORTANT IF YOUR GROUP HAS MORE THAN EIGHT PEOPLE. WRITE PRAYER REQUESTS ON THE *SMALL GROUP PRAYER AND PRAISE REPORTS*, PAGE 69.

*1. As you close your meeting, take time to pray for each other. For some of you, praying in a group may be a new experience; that's okay. Try praying just one sentence, something like "Thank you, Lord, for showing me a new perspective on my problems."

2. Pray for those who shared struggles they are facing. Also pray for those you want to invite to join the group at the next meeting.

Before You Leave

1. Take a few minutes to look at the *Small Group Calendar* in the *Small Group Resources* section, page 71. Healthy groups share responsibilities and group ownership. Fill out the calendar together noting where you will meet each week, who will facilitate, and who will provide a meal or snack. Note special events, socials, or days off as well. (Group Coordinator would be a great role for someone in your group!)

2. Also, start collecting basic contact information like phone numbers and e-mail addresses. The group roster (called "*My Small Group*") on the inside cover of your study guide is a good place to keep this information. Pass the study guides around the circle and have the members provide information about themselves.

Additional Study

This section is for those who would like to dig a little deeper. If time allows, work through it together as a group, or assign it as homework and discuss it later.

1. James' words about trials having purpose in our lives (James 1:3–4) do not introduce a new concept. We see this thought throughout Scripture. Read each of the following passages and note what God says about our trials and suffering.
   • Matthew 5:11–12
   • Romans 5:3–5
   • Hebrews 12:11
   • 1 Peter 1:6–7

2. Share any conclusions you can draw from the previous verses about the benefits or purposes of trials.

*3. In 2 Corinthians, Paul gives us further insight regarding the profit or purpose of suffering. Read the following verses and identify lessons about persevering that Paul learned from his life experiences.
   • 2 Corinthians 1:8–9
   • 2 Corinthians 12:7–10

Preparation for Next Time

1. Read James 1:5–11.

2. Be sure to invite the friends you prayed for this week. Offer to pick them up and be sure to get each of them a study guide before the meeting.

3. Work on memorizing this week's Memory Verse and be ready to say it to someone at the next meeting. (All of the *Memory Verses* from this study of James are listed on page 76 in the *Small Group Resources* section.) A simple way to memorize Scripture is to handwrite the verse between five and eight times on a piece of paper. This simple practice will strengthen your faith in God.

2

SESSION TWO:
HOW TO MAKE UP
YOUR MIND
JAMES 1:5–11

SESSION TWO — JAMES 1:5–11

HOST TIP: IF YOUR GROUP IS UNABLE TO WORK THROUGH THE ENTIRE SESSION, WE HAVE RECOMMENDED ONE QUESTION OR ACTIVITY WITH AN ASTERISK (*) IN EACH SECTION OF THE STUDY.

Connect ....15 minutes

1. If anyone has joined your group this week, welcome each one and have everybody introduce themselves.

*2. Briefly describe a time in your life when your indecision got you in trouble. What were the consequences?

Grow ....45 minutes

Memory Verse

[5]If any of you lacks wisdom, he should ask God,
who gives generously to all without finding fault, and it will be given to him.
[6]But when he asks, he must believe and not doubt, because he who doubts is like a
wave of the sea, blown and tossed by the wind.
James 1:5–6 (NIV)

Watch the video now. Follow along in your Bibles and take notes on the outline.

⁵If any of you lacks wisdom, he should ask God, who gives generously to all without finding fault, and it will be given to him. ⁶But when he asks, he must believe and not doubt, because he who doubts is like a wave of the sea, blown and tossed by the wind. ⁷That man should not think he will receive anything from the Lord; ⁸he is a double-minded man, unstable in all he does. ⁹The brother in humble circumstances ought to take pride in his high position. ¹⁰But the one who is rich should take pride in his low position, because he will pass away like a wild flower. ¹¹For the sun rises with scorching heat and withers the plant; its blossom falls and its beauty is destroyed. In the same way, the rich man will fade away even while he goes about his business. (James 1:5–11 NIV)

The Problem: _____ *Indecision*

A double-minded man is unstable in all his ways. (James 1:8 KJV)

decide–choose

Indecision causes . . .

1. Unstable *life style–emotions*
2. Unstable *relationships*
3. Unstable *spiritual life*

The Prescription: *Get wisdom – ask God*

Three Steps to Getting Wisdom

1. _____ *admit* _____ my need.

If any of you lacks wisdom . . . (James 1:5a NIV)

Definition of Wisdom: Seeing life from God's *point of view*

When pride comes, then comes disgrace, but with humility comes wisdom.
(Proverbs 11:2 NIV)

wisdom is knowing what to do with knowledge

2. _____ *Ask* _____ for it.

If any man lacks wisdom, he should ask God . . . (James 1:5a NIV)

It is the LORD who gives wisdom; from him come knowledge and understanding. (Proverbs 2:6 GN)

3. _____ *anticipate* _____ it.

⁵If any of you lacks wisdom, he should ask God, who gives generously to all without finding fault, and it will be given to him. ⁶But when he asks, he must believe and not doubt, . . . (James 1:5–6a NIV)

And without faith it is impossible to please God, because anyone who comes to him must believe that he exists, and that he rewards those who earnestly seek him. (Hebrews 11:6 NIV)

The Promise: _God will give it_

How God Gives Wisdom

If any of you lacks wisdom, he should ask God, who gives generously to all without finding fault, . . . (James 1:5 NIV)

1. _Continually_
2. _generously_
3. _without finding fault_

Discussion Questions

1. Based on James' definition of the "*double-minded man*" (verse 8), why do you think this kind of person is so offensive to God?

2. According to James 1:5, what is the solution to the problem of indecision?

*3. What promise does God make to those who ask him for wisdom? What conditions does God attach to this promise?

4. Fear, pride, forgetfulness, unbelief, doubts, laziness, and a lack of understanding God, may be among the things that keep us from asking God for wisdom. What keeps you from asking God for wisdom? What do you think can change this and enable you to go quickly to the Lord for wisdom?

Serve . . . . .10 minutes

Discovering where you best fit in ministry requires seeking God's wisdom. The Bible gives us good news when it tells us God is willing to give the wisdom we need when we ask him for help.

1. God's Word says that the Holy Spirit (1 Corinthians 2:9–12; John 14:26, 16:13–14), the Word of God (Psalm 119:97–105, 2 Timothy 3:16–17), meditation on God's Word (Psalm 1:1–3), wise counsel (Proverbs 15:22), and prayer (Romans 8:26–27) can all be sources of God's wisdom. Which items on this list have helped you learn where you can best serve God and other people?

*2. Just as it is important to have an accurate picture of what God is like, you also need to have an accurate picture of your own spiritual life. To help you evaluate your spiritual life, take a few minutes to complete the *Purpose Driven Health Assessment* (found on page 72 in the *Small Group Resources* section). This tool will help you perform a quick checkup of your spiritual health. After answering each question, tally your results. If you are comfortable doing so, share with your group one area you are doing well in and one area where you would like to grow.

Share . . . . .10 minutes

Often we struggle with indecision because we lack the wisdom we need to feel confident about our choices. At times like this, we may need to deal with our pride or fear, admit our need, and ask God to give us his wisdom. James tells us that God promises to give wisdom to those who ask.

*1. What wrong attitudes about asking God for wisdom can hinder our ability to share Christ with others?

2. Why is God's wisdom the key to success as we share the Good News with those around us?

Worship . . . . .15 minutes

When we realize that God desires to give us wisdom when we ask him for it, our first response should be gratitude. God is pleased when we are grateful, thankful children showing our trust and faith in him. Bringing such pleasure to God is called "worship."

1. Take a few minutes as a group to praise and thank God for his willingness to meet all your needs. Thank him especially for his wisdom.

*2. Pray for one another, especially about those areas of your lives where you each need God's wisdom this week. Record the needs and prayer requests of the group members on the *Prayer and Praise Report* in the *Small Group Resources* section on page 69.

Additional Study

As we have seen, trials are designed to test our faith, increase our endurance, and perfect our character. In our study last week, James called us to consider this process "joy" because it can cause us to grow. Then he spoke of the results of our trials.

*1. If possible, use a Vine's Expository Dictionary or some other word study reference (even a Webster's Dictionary will offer further insights) to look up some of the words James uses in verses 3 and 4 to describe the results we gain from experiencing trials:

  • Perseverance

  • Maturity

  • Completion

  In what ways can our awareness of these results affect what we learn from our suffering, trials, and tests?

2. After assuring us that we can grow as a result of our trials, James speaks to us about wisdom. Discuss your thoughts about the difference between wisdom and knowledge. (You could also have someone look up *wisdom* and *knowledge* in the dictionary.)

  • Wisdom

  • Knowledge

3. Why do you think James brings the idea of wisdom into a discussion of trials?

*4. Read Proverbs 9:10–12. What are the blessings and benefits of having wisdom?

Preparation For Next Time

1. Read James 1:12–18.

2. If you haven't yet completed the *Purpose Driven Health Assessment* on page 72, take time this week to answer the questions and evaluate your spiritual health. Ask God for wisdom about what changes he would have you make in light of the results. If you are on track, take time to praise him.

3. Continue to pray for those friends you've thought about inviting to this study. Be sure to invite them again. You never know: Yours may be the most important telephone call they get all year.

4. Remember to pray for the group members' needs you wrote down last week on the *Prayer and Praise Report* page in the *Small Group Resources* section.

3

Session Three:
How to Win
Over Temptation
James 1:12–18

Connect . . . . .15 minutes

The Christian life is often talked about in sports terms. The athlete who trains for competition has to persevere through pain, fatigue, and discouragement, yet the hope of a reward keeps the athlete motivated. In the same way, every Christian who perseveres through trials and withstands life's tests receives a prize. James calls it a crown—the crown of eternal life with our Lord.

*1. Briefly describe a time when you worked hard to achieve a goal. What did it take to succeed, and what motivated you to persevere?

2. At your current stage of life, what goal is most important for you to achieve? Why?

Grow . . . . .45 Minutes

Memory Verse
Blessed is the man who perseveres under trial,
because when he has stood the test,
he will receive the crown of life that God has promised to those who love him.
James 1:12 (NIV)

Watch the video now. Follow along in your Bibles and take notes on the outline.

Two Kinds of Testing

• Trials from _____God_____; designed to cause growth.

• Temptations from _____Devil_____; designed to cause sin.

¹²Blessed is the man who perseveres under trial, because when he has stood the test, he will receive the crown of life that God has promised to those who love him. ¹³When tempted, no one should say, "God is tempting me." For God cannot be tempted by evil, nor does he tempt anyone; ¹⁴but each one is tempted when, by his own evil desire, he is dragged away and enticed. ¹⁵Then, after desire has conceived, it gives birth to sin; and sin, when it is full-grown, gives birth to death. ¹⁶Don't be deceived, my dear brothers. ¹⁷Every good and perfect gift is from above, coming down from the Father of the heavenly lights, who does not change like shifting shadows. ¹⁸He chose to give us birth through the word of truth, that we might be a kind of firstfruits of all he created. (James 1:12–18 NIV)

How Can I Win Over Temptation?

1. Be ___realistic___.

   No temptation has seized you except what is common to man.
   (1 Corinthians 10:13a NIV)

   (Jesus) . . . was in all points tempted like as we are, yet without sin.
   (Hebrews 4:15 KJV)

2. Be ___responsible___.

   When tempted, no one should say, "God is tempting me." For God cannot be tempted by evil, nor does he tempt anyone. (James 1:13 NIV)

3. Be ___ready___.

   Each one is tempted when, by his own evil desire, he is dragged away and enticed . . . Don't be deceived, my dear brothers. (James 1:14–16 NIV)

   . . . in order that Satan might not outwit us. For we are not unaware of his schemes.
   (2 Corinthians 2:11 NIV)

Four Steps the Devil Uses To Tempt Us

Step 1: _Desire_

... *each one is tempted when, by his own evil desire* ... (James 1:14a NIV)

Step 3: _Deception_

... *he is dragged away and enticed.* (James 1:14b NIV)

Step 3: _Disobedience_

Then, after desire has conceived, it gives birth to sin ... (James 1:15a NIV)

Step 4: _Death (spiritual separation from God_

... *and sin, when full grown, gives birth to death.* (James 1:15b NIV)

Every good and perfect gift is from above, coming down from the Father of the heavenly lights, who does not change like shifting shadows. (James 1:17 NIV)

4. Be _refocused_ .

5. Be _reborn_ .

He chose to give us birth through the word of truth, that we might be a kind of firstfruits of all he created. (James 1:18 NIV)

God is faithful; he will not let you be tempted beyond what you can bear. But when you are tempted, he will also provide a way out so that you can stand up under it. (1 Corinthians 10:13b NIV)

Resources To Resist Temptation

1. _Fellowship_ with other Christians.

2. Get into the _____ .

Discussion Questions

1. Some pitfalls we Christians face are (1) denying our vulnerability to temptation and (2) failing to take responsibility for our own actions. What does James say is the source of temptations that come our way?

2. Which of our legitimate desires does Satan tempt us to fulfill in illegitimate ways?

*3. 1 John 2:16 describes the process of temptation as the lust of the flesh (to do), the lust of the eyes (to have), and the pride of life (to be). What are some everyday examples of how we are faced with these temptations?

4. In what ways do our thoughts affect our ability to overcome temptations? What do we need to focus on in order to successfully resist temptation?

Serve . . . . .10 minutes

Our love for God and our commitment to serve him do not keep us from facing temptations in this life. In fact, Jesus, Paul, and James call us again and again to "be on your guard," ready and watchful for things that might cause us harm.

1. According to Matthew 26:41 and Ephesians 6:10–18, what can you do to avoid falling into temptation? Which of these admonitions do you think is most important for you to be mindful of as you serve God and others?

Share . . . . .10 minutes

As Christians, we must be watchful and ready to resist all temptations that come our way. One reason is that people around us are watching to see if we are living according to God's standards.

1. When has another believer's way of life been a real encouragement to your faith? What did you learn from that person's lifestyle about walking with the Lord and being his representative?

*2. What commitment do you need to make to God and to yourself in order to protect his good name as you represent him to the world around you? Share your commitment with the group and ask them to pray for you.

Worship . . . . .10 minutes

Surrendering your heart to God is essential to gaining control over temptation and your thought life. And a surrendered life is a life of worship.

1. Spend a few moments in prayer asking God to show you one area of your life you need to fully surrender to him. Maybe you need to acknowledge your sins, recognize that Jesus died in your place as punishment for that sin, and invite him to be your Savior and your Lord. Maybe you are especially vulnerable to temptation in a specific area of your life and you need God's power to resist. Maybe you need to spend more time studying God's Word and filling your mind with his thoughts so you can more easily resist temptation. If you are willing to more fully surrender your life and your heart to God, share that decision either with the group now or with your host after the meeting.

*2. As you close your meeting, take time to pray for each other. Pray for those who shared their struggles. Ask God to help each of you to be realistic about your vulnerability to sin. Pray that God will give you courage to take responsibility for your actions, and to resist temptation. Finally, be certain that members of your group understand the gospel. Give any who haven't received Jesus as Lord and Savior the opportunity to do so and be born again.

Additional Study

Although the Bible uses the same Greek word to speak of both "tests" and "temptations," the context usually reveals what God wants us to see. God uses tests or trials to grow us in our faith. Satan uses temptations to try to cause us to sin. Trials and temptations are part of everyone's life. When we recognize and remember their purpose, we will see God use them to grow us into the people he wants us to be.

Let's take a closer look at what James tells us about the source of temptation.

1. According to James 1:14, what is the root of temptation?

2. What is the ultimate result of that temptation, as stated in James 1:15?

3. Do you think James is saying the devil doesn't tempt us? Read James 4:7–8 for further insight about the devil and our temptations.

4. Do you think these two passages (James 1:14–15 and James 4:7–8) contradict each other? Why or why not?

*5. James 1:17 says God is the source of "*every good and perfect gift.*" What gifts might help us deal with our evil desires? Look up the following verses for some hints.

• James 1:5

• Matthew 7:7–8, Luke 22:40

• Psalm 119:11

33

Preparation For Next Time

1. Read James 1:19–27.

2. Review the commitments you made during Session 3. Make a plan for following through on those commitments and prepare to share your progress with the group the next time you meet.

3. If you have a spiritual partner, update him or her on how your walk with the Lord is going. Be sure to use most of your time praying for one another.

4. Remember to pray this week for the needs and commitments of your group members.

5. Work on memorizing the Memory Verse from Session 3.

SESSION FOUR:
HOW TO BE BLESSED
BY THE BIBLE

JAMES 1:19–27

Connect . . . . .10 minutes

*1. In Luke 8:4–15 Jesus compared the Word of God to a seed planted in the "soil" of our hearts. What was the condition of the soil of your heart the first time you heard about Jesus and God's plan of salvation?

Grow . . . . .45 minutes

Memory Verse

But the man who looks intently into the perfect law that gives freedom,
and continues to do this, not forgetting what he has heard,
but doing it—he will be blessed in what he does.
James 1:25 (NIV)

Watch the video now. Follow along in your Bibles and take notes on the outline.

¹⁹My dear brothers, take note of this: Everyone should be quick to listen, slow to speak and slow to become angry, ²⁰for man's anger does not bring about the righteous life that God desires. ²¹Therefore, get rid of all moral filth and the evil that is so prevalent and humbly accept the word planted in you, which can save you. ²²Do not merely listen to the word, and so deceive yourselves. Do what it says. ²³Anyone who listens to the word but does not do what it says is like a man who looks at his face in a mirror ²⁴and, after looking at himself, goes away and immediately forgets what he looks like. ²⁵But the man who looks intently into the perfect law that gives freedom, and continues to do this, not forgetting what he has heard, but doing it—he will be blessed in what he does. ²⁶If anyone considers himself religious and yet does not keep a tight rein on his tongue, he deceives himself and his religion is worthless. ²⁷Religion that God our Father accepts as pure and faultless is this: to look after orphans and widows in their distress and to keep oneself from being polluted by the world. (James 1:19–27 NIV)

I Must _____ God's Word

Four Attitudes to Prepare Your Heart:

1. Be _____ .

   Be quick to listen, slow to speak . . . (James 1:19a NIV)

2. Be _____ .

   . . . and slow to become angry . . . (James 1:19b NIV)

3. Be _____ .

   Get rid of all moral filth and the evil that is so prevalent and humbly accept the word planted in you, which can save you. (James 1:21 NIV)

4. Be _____ .

I Must _____ on God's Word

1. _____ it.

   The man who looks intently into the perfect law . . . (James 1:25a NIV)

S.P.A.C.E.P.E.T.S. — Nine things to look for as you gaze intently into the Word of God:

S - Is there a **S**in to confess?

P - Is there a **P**romise to claim?

A - Is there an **A**ttitude to change?

C - Is there a **C**ommand to keep?

E - Is there an **E**xample to follow?

P - Is there a **P**rayer to pray?

E - Is there an **E**rror to avoid?

T - Is there a **T**ruth to believe?

S - Is there **S**omething to thank God for?

2. _____ it.

   . . . and continues to do this . . . (James 1:25b NIV)

3. _____ it.

   . . . not forgetting what he has heard . . . (James 1:25b NIV)

I Must _____ to God's Word

Do not merely listen to the word, and so deceive yourselves. Do what it says. (James 1:22 NIV)

He puts that law into practice and he wins true happiness. (James 1:25 PH)

"Now that you know these things, you will be blessed if you do them." (John 13:17 NIV)

I Must _____ the Word

1. _____ mouth
2. _____ heart
3. _____ mind

Discussion Questions

*1. Why is listening such an important skill for Christians? How can being *"quick to listen"* and *"slow to speak"* (verse 19) keep our anger from erupting? In what ways can our uncontrolled anger affect our witness of Christ in our lives?

2. Why is it important for us believers to rid ourselves of *"all moral filth"* and *"evil"* (verse 21)? What are some practical ways we can do this?

3. What do you think it means to *"humbly accept the word?"* (verse 21). What word is James referring to; and how is it planted in us?

4. James says, *"Do not merely listen to the word, and so deceive yourselves. Do what it says"* (1:22). If we do not allow the Word of God to change us, we cannot expect to be blessed. Give an example of how your life has been blessed when you put into practice something you learned from studying the Bible. What are some practical ways you can respond to what you've learned in this session's study of God's Word?

Serve . . . . .10 minutes

*1. To begin putting into practice what you have heard in God's Word, what is one thing that you could do this week to minister to the needs of someone around you? Be specific—and then do it!

Share . . . . .15 Minutes

*1. What might people who do not know you are a Christian notice about you that makes you different from other people?

2. As we attempt to share Christ at home, at work, in the community, or even abroad, why is it important that our lives reflect Christ in practical ways? What are some actions that will speak louder than our words?

Worship . . . . .15 minutes

*1. Pair up with one other person and take a few moments to pray for each other. (We strongly recommend that men partner with men and women partner with women.) Ask God to show you one area of your life that needs to be changed by his Word. Then ask him to prepare your heart for the change he wants to make in your life.

2. Close your meeting by praying together as a group. Pray for those group members who shared struggles they are facing.

Additional Study

How much of God's Word are you actually applying to your life? One of the reasons we don't do a better job of applying God's Word in our everyday life is that we have not prepared ourselves to hear his Word.

1. According to verses 19-21 how can we prepare ourselves to hear God's Word?

2. List the commands, the "Do's and Don'ts," James gives in 1:19–27. Spend a few minutes defining in practical terms what these commands mean. (To gain further insight you may want to look up some of the words in Vine's Expository Dictionary or Webster's Dictionary.)

*3. Talk about . . .

• A time when you were really prepared to hear the Word of God, and it changed your life.

• A time when hearing the truth caused you to become defensive.

• A time when your heart was hardened to the truth and you missed a lesson that would have protected you from a wrong decision or unpleasant situation.

Preparation for Next Time

1. Read James 2:1–13.

2. Memorize this week's Memory Verse and be prepared to share it with your group.

3. Review any commitments you made this week and make a specific plan for following through on those commitments.

4. Pray for the needs of the people in your group.

5

SESSION FIVE:
HOW TO TREAT
PEOPLE RIGHT

JAMES 2:1–13

CONNECT ....15 minutes

1. Briefly describe a time when you felt unwelcome in a new environment. What did it feel like and how did you respond?

*2. Take a few minutes to discuss whether or not you will continue meeting as a group after the next and final session of this study. If so, will you continue on with Volume 2 of the James study, or will you choose something else? Who will lead? When and where will you meet?

Grow ....45 minutes

Memory Verse
If you really keep the royal law found in Scripture,
"Love your neighbor as yourself," you are doing right. But if you show favoritism,
you sin and are convicted by the law as lawbreakers.
James 2:8–9 (NIV)

Watch the video now. Follow along in your Bibles and take notes on the outline.

¹*My brothers, as believers in our glorious Lord Jesus Christ, don't show favoritism. ²Suppose a man comes into your meeting wearing a gold ring and fine clothes, and a poor man in shabby clothes also comes in. ³If you show special attention to the man wearing fine clothes and say, "Here's a good seat for you," but say to the poor man, "You stand there" or "Sit on the floor by my feet," ⁴have you not discriminated among yourselves and become judges with evil thoughts? ⁵Listen, my dear brothers: Has not God chosen those who are poor in the eyes of the world to be rich in faith and to inherit the kingdom he promised those who love him? ⁶But you have insulted the poor. Is it not the rich who are exploiting you? Are they not the ones who are dragging you into court? ⁷Are they not the ones who are slandering the noble name of him to whom you belong? ⁸If you really keep the royal law found in Scripture, "Love your neighbor as yourself," you are doing right. ⁹But if you show favoritism, you sin and are convicted by the law as lawbreakers. ¹⁰For whoever keeps the whole law and yet stumbles at just one point is guilty of breaking all of it. ¹¹For he who said, "Do not commit adultery," also said, "Do not murder." If you do not commit adultery but do commit murder, you have become a lawbreaker. ¹²Speak and act as those who are going to be judged by the law that gives freedom, ¹³because judgment without mercy will be shown to anyone who has not been merciful. Mercy triumphs over judgment!* (James 2:1–13 NIV)

The Principle: Don't Show Favoritism

Ways We Show Favoritism

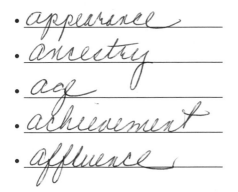

- appearance
- ancestry
- age
- achievement
- affluence

Three Problems with Showing Favoritism

1. Favoritism is _____unchristian_____.

   For God does not show favoritism. (Romans 2:11 NIV)

2. Favoritism is _____unreasonable_____.

   Has not God chosen those who are poor . . . to be rich in faith . . . and inherit the kingdom . . . ? (James 2:5 NIV)

3. Favoritism is _____unloving_____.

   If you really keep the royal law found in Scripture, "Love your neighbor as yourself," you are doing right. (James 2:8 NIV)

   The entire law is summed up in a single command: "Love your neighbor as yourself." (Galatians 5:14 NIV)

The Prescription for How to Overcome Favoritism

Accept one another, then, just as Christ accepted you. (Romans 15:7a NIV)

1. _____Accept_____ everybody.

2. _____Appreciate_____ everybody.

   Do nothing out of selfish ambition or vain conceit, but in humility consider others better than yourselves. Each of you should look not only to your own interests, but also the interests of others. (Philippians 2:3–4 NIV)

3. _____Affirm_____ everybody.

   Encourage one another and build each other up . . . (1 Thessalonians 5:11a NIV)

Discussion Questions

1. Describe some ways in which we in the church show favoritism today.

2. What is God's view of favoritism? In what ways is favoritism *"judgment without mercy"* (verse 13), and what kind of judgment will God bring on those who show favoritism?

3. According to James 2:8, what is *"the royal law found in Scripture"*? Why is showing favoritism a violation of this law?

*4. What is God nudging you personally to do to become more accepting, appreciative, or affirming of others? What practical steps can you take to help others feel God's love and acceptance?

Serve ....10 minutes

*1. If we are to minister to the needs of people in our community, we must be willing to show them unconditional love when they come to our church. If they arrive and no one speaks to them or offers a handshake, they are not likely to return and give us a second chance to ignore them. A friendly face and a word of welcome might be the very thing that encourages them to come back. Do you make it a practice to welcome unfamiliar people to your church? If not, why not? If so, why?

2. Discuss whether your group would like to have a potluck or other type of social to celebrate what God has been doing in your group during this study. You might share a meal before your final group meeting, or you could have a dessert or snack party after you finish the final lesson in Volume 1 next week.

Share . . . . .10 minutes

Recently, 8,600 people from congregations in 39 different denominations were surveyed concerning their "love quotient." What was discovered? Churches that had learned how to love people were growing, while those that hadn't learned how to love people were declining. The amount of love and acceptance people experience when they attend church significantly influences that church's growth or decline.

1. Spend a few minutes evaluating how well you are doing as a group in loving and accepting others in your small group and in your church. What specific things can members of your group do to ensure that both new and current group members feel accepted, appreciated, and affirmed when they are with you?

Worship . . . . .10 minutes

Worship is caring about what God cares about. We please God when we show love to others.

*1. Spend some time in prayer with your whole group.

- Thank God for not showing favoritism, but for saving you from your sins and giving you new life in Christ.

- Ask God to bring new people to your church.

- Ask God to give you his heart for people, so that your church will not show favoritism, but will be a place that welcomes everyone, whatever their social status or history.

2. Close in an attitude of prayer by singing *Amazing Grace*.

> *Amazing grace, how sweet the sound*
> *That saved a wretch like me*
> *I once was lost but now am found*
> *Was blind but now I see*
>
> *'Twas grace that taught my heart to fear*
> *And grace my fears relieved*
> *How precious did that grace appear*
> *The hour I first believed*
>
> *The Lord has promised good to me*
> *His word my hope secures*
> *He will my shield and portion be*
> *As long as life endures*

Words by John Newton, Music:
19th Century American Melody, Public Domain

Additional Study

As we've seen, James has much to say about favoritism and the way we treat one another. No one likes to see people playing favorites, but favoritism on the part of Christians is particularly offensive because we are Christ's representatives. Christ's example to us was not one of favoritism. Jesus was clear about how we should treat people.

1. Note the specific commands, exhortations, and examples that James presents in the following verses.

   - James 2:1

   - James 2:4

   - James 2:5

   - James 2:6–7

   - James 2:8–11

2. Read Matthew 7:1–2 and James 2:13. What do these passages teach about judgment and mercy?

*3. Ask God to show you if you are judging anyone without mercy. Confess that sin and ask God to change your heart.

Preparation for Next Time

1. Read James 2:14–26.

2. Spend some time memorizing the Memory Verse from Session 5.

6

SESSION SIX:
HOW TO HAVE
REAL FAITH

JAMES 2:14–26

CONNECT .... .15 minutes

*1. Today's lesson is the last session in Volume 1 of the study of James. Take some time to review the *Purpose Driven Group Guidelines* (page 66). Discuss how the sessions have gone and any changes you would like to make to your group format. Talk about what you would like to study next, who will lead, and where you will meet. Visit **www.PurposeDriven.com** to order Volume 2 of the James study and to check out the many other video-based small group studies we have produced at Purpose Driven Ministries. If you are planning a social gathering for a seventh session of this study, be sure everyone knows the details.

*2. Before you came to know Jesus as your Savior, how did you think people got into heaven? For instance, was it just by being a good person, or by keeping the Ten Commandments, or by going to church regularly, or maybe something else?

Grow .... .45 minutes

Memory Verse
In the same way, faith by itself,
if it is not accompanied by action, is dead.
James 2:17 (NIV)

Watch the video now. Follow along in your Bibles and take notes on the outline.

14What good is it, my brothers, if a man claims to have faith but has no deeds? Can such faith save him? 15Suppose a brother or sister is without clothes and daily food. 16If one of you says to him, "Go, I wish you well; keep warm and well fed," but does nothing about his physical needs, what good is it? 17In the same way, faith by itself, if it is not accompanied by action, is dead. 18But someone will say, "You have faith; I have deeds." Show me your faith without deeds, and I will show you my faith by what I do. 19You believe that there is one God. Good! Even the demons believe that—and shudder. 20You foolish man, do you want evidence that faith without deeds is useless? 21Was not our ancestor Abraham considered righteous for what he did when he offered his son Isaac on the altar? 22You see that his faith and his actions were working together, and his faith was made complete by what he did. 23And the scripture was fulfilled that says, "Abraham believed God, and it was credited to him as righteousness," and he was called God's friend. 24You see that a person is justified by what he does and not by faith alone. 25In the same way, was not even Rahab the prostitute considered righteous for what she did when she gave lodging to the spies and sent them off in a different direction? 26As the body without the spirit is dead, so faith without deeds is dead. (James 2:14–26 NIV)

What Paul and James Say About Faith and Works

Paul	James
Paul	**James**
Fighting _____	Fighting _____
"Works" = Jewish _____	"Works" = Christian _____
"Faith" = _____ of salvation	"Works" = _____ of salvation
How to _____ you're a Christian	How to _____ you're a Christian
How to _____ a believer	How to _____ a believer

8For it is by God's grace that you have been saved through faith. 10 . . . for a life of good deeds, which he has already prepared for us to do. (Ephesians 2:8, 10 GN)

What is Real Faith?

1. Real faith is not just something you _____ .

   What good is it, my brothers, if a man claims to have faith but has no deeds? Can such faith save him? (James 2:14 NIV)

2. Real faith is not just something you _____ .

   ¹⁵Suppose a brother or sister is without clothes and daily food. ¹⁶If one of you says to him, "Go, I wish you well; keep warm and well fed," but does nothing about his physical needs, what good is it? (James 2:15–16 NIV)

   If anyone has material possessions and sees his brother in need but has no pity on him, how can the love of God be in him? (1 John 3:17 NIV)

   In the same way, faith by itself, if it is not accompanied by action, is dead. (James 2:17 NIV)

3. Real faith is not just something you _____ .

   But someone will say, "You have faith; I have deeds." (James 2:18a NIV)

   Show me your faith without deeds, and I will show you my faith by what I do. (James 2:18b NIV)

4. Real faith is not just something you _____ .

   You believe that there is one God. Good! Even the demons believe that—and shudder! (James 2:19 NIV)

   The fool says in his heart, "There is no God." (Psalm 14:1a NIV)

5. Real faith is something you _____ .

   ²⁰You foolish man, do you want evidence that faith without deeds is useless? ²¹Was not our ancestor Abraham considered righteous for what he did when he offered his son Isaac on the altar? ²²ᵃYou see that his faith and his actions were working together . . . (James 2:20–22a NIV)

   Examine yourselves to see whether you are in the faith; test yourselves. (2 Corinthians 13:5a NIV)

DISCUSSION QUESTIONS

[8]For it is by grace you have been saved, through faith—and this not from yourselves, it is the gift of God—[9]not by works, so that no one can boast. [10]For we are God's workmanship, created in Christ Jesus to do good works, which God prepared in advance for us to do. (Ephesians 2:8–10 NIV)

Know that a man is not justified by observing the law, but by faith in Jesus Christ. So we, too, have put our faith in Christ Jesus that we may be justified by faith in Christ and not by observing the law, because by observing the law no one will be justified. (Galatians 2:16 NIV)

1. Compare James' teaching in James 2:14–26 with what Paul says in Ephesians 2:8–10 and Galatians 2:16. Identify the key points and explain how their views about works fit together.

2. According to Paul and James, what is the evidence that you are truly a believer?

*3. As you think about James' exhortation to do what the Word teaches, what proof do you see in your life that your confession of faith in Christ is real? If you asked the people closest to you, what evidence of a genuine faith in Christ would they point to in your life?

Serve . . . .**15 minutes**

Paul clearly states in Ephesians 2:8 that we're saved by grace through faith: We're saved simply by accepting in faith God's gift of forgiveness through Jesus Christ. Our faith is not *determined* by what we do, it is *demonstrated* by what we do. So what do we do that shows we are believers?

1. Identify some changes in your life since you accepted Jesus as your Savior. In what ways is your lifestyle different from the unbelievers around you? Be specific.

*2. Identify someone in your group or church family who has a practical need. You could also ask your pastor or another church leader about any needs your group could meet. Then, discuss what you can do together to meet that need.

Share . . . .**15 minutes**

*1. Why is obedience to the command "Love your neighbor as yourself" important to helping others come to know Christ? Tell of a time when someone came to Christ because Christ's love was demonstrated in a very practical way.

2. If you personally haven't accepted Christ as your Savior and Lord, be sure to talk to someone about what is holding you back. If you have recently accepted Christ, what is your next step in your Christian life (e.g., being baptized, joining the church, etc.)?

Worship . . . .**20 minutes**

If you're planning a seventh meeting as a time of celebration, save this first discussion point until then.

1. What has God revealed to you about himself over the past six weeks? What have you learned about yourself? What are the highlights of this study of James 1–2?

*2. Take a few minutes to affirm your group leaders and thank God for them.

3. Close by thanking God for what he taught you through your study of James. Pray for any needs of your group. Write your prayer requests on the *Prayer and Praise Report* pages provided in the *Small Group Resources* section, page 69.

Additional Study

Let's look together at what Paul, John, Jesus, and James have to say about salvation, and see if we can clarify the relationship of faith and works. Have various members of the group read aloud the verses in the following questions. Listen for the key thoughts in each passage.

1. According to Paul's teaching in Galatians 5:6, what is "*genuine faith*"? Record your observations on the chart on the next page.

2. According to 1 John 3:10, 17–19, what is clear evidence that we "*belong to the truth*"? Add your findings to the chart.

3. Record what Jesus said about faith and deeds in Matthew 7:15–23, 25:31–46.

4. Now add James' thoughts on the relationship between faith and deeds from James 1:27 and 2:14–17.

Paul	John	Jesus	James

5. What harmony do you see between the teachings of Paul, John, Jesus, and James on the subject of faith and works?

*6. As a group, brainstorm for a few minutes to come up with a clear explanation of how salvation is connected to faith and works.

GROUP
DEVELOPMENT:
SMALL GROUP RESOURCES

Helps for Hosts

Top Ten Ideas for New Hosts

Congratulations! As the host of your small group, you have responded to the call to help shepherd Jesus' flock. Few other tasks in the family of God surpass the contribution you will be making.

As you prepare to facilitate your group, whether it is one session or the entire series, here are a few thoughts to keep in mind. We encourage you to read and review these tips with each new discussion host before he or she leads.

Remember you are not alone. God knows everything about you, and he knew you would be asked to facilitate your group. Even though you may not feel ready, this is common for all good hosts. God promises, *"I will never leave you; I will never abandon you"* (Hebrews 13:5 TEV). Whether you are facilitating for one evening, several weeks, or a lifetime, you will be blessed as you serve.

1. **Don't try to do it alone.** Pray right now for God to help you build a healthy team. If you can enlist a co-host to help you shepherd the group, you will find your experience much richer. This is your chance to involve as many people as you can in building a healthy group. All you have to do is ask people to help. You'll be surprised at the response.

2. **Be friendly and be yourself.** God wants to use your unique gifts and temperament. Be sure to greet people at the door with a big smile . . . this can set the mood for the whole gathering. Remember, they are taking as big a step as you are to show up at your house! Don't try to do things exactly like another host; do them in a way that fits you. Admit when you don't have an answer and apologize when you make a mistake. Your group will love you for it and you'll sleep better at night.

3. **Prepare for your meeting ahead of time.** Watch the video session before your group arrives. Write down your responses to each question. Pay special attention to exercises that ask group members to do something other than engage in discussion. These exercises will help your group live what the Bible teaches, not just talk about it. Be sure you understand how an exercise works. If the exercise employs one of the items in the *Small Group Resource* section (such as the *Group Guidelines*), be sure to look over that item so you'll know how it works.

4. **Pray for your group members by name.** Before you begin your session, take a few moments and pray for each member by name. You may want to review the prayer list at least once a week. Ask God to use your time together to touch the heart of every person in your group. Expect God to lead you to whomever he wants you to encourage or challenge in a special way. If you listen, God will surely lead.

5. **When you ask a question, be patient.** Someone will eventually respond. Sometimes people need a moment or two of silence to think about the question. If silence doesn't bother you, it won't bother anyone else. After someone responds, affirm the response with a simple "thanks" or "great answer." Then ask, "How about somebody else?" or "Would someone who hasn't shared like to add anything?" Be sensitive to new people or reluctant members who aren't ready to say, pray, or do anything. If you give them a safe setting, they will blossom over time. If someone in your group is a "wall flower" who sits silently through every session, consider talking to them privately and encouraging them to participate. Let them know how important they are to you—that they are loved and appreciated, and that the group would value their input. Remember, still water often runs deep.

6. **Provide transitions between questions.** Ask if anyone would like to read the paragraph or Bible passage. Don't call on anyone, but ask for a volunteer, and then be patient until someone begins. Be sure to thank the person who reads aloud.

7. **Break into smaller groups occasionally.** The Grow and Worship sections provide good opportunities to break into smaller circles of three to five people. With a greater opportunity to talk in a small circle, people will connect more with the study, apply more quickly what they're learning, and ultimately get more out of their small group experience. A small circle also encourages a quiet person to participate and tends to minimize the effects of a more vocal or dominant member.

8. **Small circles are also helpful during prayer time.** People who are unaccustomed to praying aloud will feel more comfortable trying it with just two or three others. Also, prayer requests won't take as much time, so circles will have more time to actually pray. When you gather back with the whole group, you can have one person from each circle briefly update everyone on the prayer requests from their subgroups. The other great aspect of subgrouping is that it fosters leadership development. As you ask people in the group to facilitate discussion or to lead a prayer circle, it gives them a small leadership step that can build their confidence.

9. **Rotate facilitators occasionally.** You may be perfectly capable of hosting each time, but you will help others grow in their faith and gifts if you give them opportunities to host the group.

10. **One final challenge (for new or first-time hosts).** Before your first opportunity to lead, look up each of the six passages listed below. Read each one as a devotional exercise to help prepare you with a shepherd's heart. Trust us on this one. If you do this, you will be more than ready for your first meeting.

Matthew 9:36–38 (NIV)

[36]When Jesus saw the crowds, he had compassion on them, because they were harassed and helpless, like sheep without a shepherd. [37]Then he said to his disciples, "The harvest is plentiful but the workers are few. [38]Ask the Lord of the harvest, therefore, to send out workers into his harvest field."

John 10:14–15 (NIV)

[14]I am the good shepherd; I know my sheep and my sheep know me—[15]just as the Father knows me and I know the Father—and I lay down my life for the sheep.

1 Peter 5:2–4 (NIV)

[2]Be shepherds of God's flock that is under your care, serving as overseers—not because you must, but because you are willing, as God wants you to be; [3]not greedy for money, but eager to serve; not lording it over those entrusted to you, but being examples to the flock. [4]And when the Chief Shepherd appears, you will receive the crown of glory that will never fade away.

Philippians 2:1–5 (NIV)

[1]If you have any encouragement from being united with Christ, if any comfort from his love, if any fellowship with the Spirit, if any tenderness and compassion, [2]then make my joy complete by being like-minded, having the same love, being one in spirit and purpose. [3]Do nothing out of selfish ambition or vain conceit, but in humility consider others better than yourselves. [4]Each of you should look not only to your own interests, but also to the interests of others. [5]Your attitude should be the same as that of Jesus Christ.

Hebrews 10:23–25 (NIV)

[23]Let us hold unswervingly to the hope we profess, for he who promised is faithful. [24]And let us consider how we may spur one another on toward love and good deeds. [25]Let us not give up meeting together, as some are in the habit of doing, but let us encourage one another—and all the more as you see the Day approaching.

1 Thessalonians 2:7–8, 11–12 (NIV)

[7]But we were gentle among you, like a mother caring for her little children. [8]We loved you so much that we were delighted to share with you not only the Gospel of God but our lives as well, because you had become so dear to us. . . . [11]For you know that we dealt with each of you as a father deals with his own children, [12]encouraging, comforting and urging you to live lives worthy of God, who calls you into his kingdom and glory.

Frequently Asked Questions

Who may attend group?

Anybody you feel would benefit. As you begin, we encourage each attendee to invite at least one other friend to join. The best time to have people join the group is in the first or second week of a new study. Take some time at your first meeting to share names of friends with group members so that as a group you can pray that they might be open to attend.

How long will this group meet?

This series is six weeks long, and we encourage groups to add one additional week for a celebration. At the end of this study, each group member may decide if he or she desires to continue on for another six-week study. In your final session take time to review your Group Agreement, and discuss what study you might do next. We recommend you visit our website at **www.purposedriven.com** for more video-based small group studies.

Who is the host?

The host is the person who coordinates and facilitates your group meetings. In addition to a host, we encourage you to select one or more group members to lead your group discussions. Several other responsibilities can be rotated, including refreshments, prayer requests, worship, or keeping up with those who miss a meeting. Shared ownership in the group helps everybody grow.

Where do we find new group members for our group?

This can be an issue for groups, especially new groups starting with just a few people or existing groups that lose a few people along the way. We encourage you to brainstorm a list of people from your work, church, neighborhood, children's school, family, the gym, and so on. Then pray for the people on each member's list. Have each group member invite several people on their list. No matter how you find members, it is important to continue actively looking for new people to join your group. All groups go through some healthy attrition as a result of moves, releasing new leaders, ministry opportunities, and so forth. If the group gets too small, it runs the risk of shutting down. Remember, the next person you add just might become a friend for eternity. You never know.

How do we handle the childcare needs in our group?

Childcare needs must be handled very carefully. This is a sensitive issue. We suggest you seek creative solutions as a group. One common solution is to have the adults meet in the living room and share the cost of a baby sitter (or two) who can be with the kids in another part of the house. Another popular option is to have one home for the kids and a second home (close by) for the adults. If desired, the adults could rotate the responsibility of providing a lesson for the kids. This last option is great with school age kids and can be a huge blessing to families.

What if we cannot get through all the content each week?

The curriculum is provided to serve you as a group and as a host. Do not feel obligated to get through all the content in this study guide. Be sensitive to the leading of the Holy Spirit during your group meeting. Some items will be more applicable for your group than others. Choose those items that best fit your group life. However, if an item stretches you as a group, do not ignore it. New experiences will breathe new growth and community into your small group.

Many groups are able to complete these study guides in the suggested six weeks, while others take several extra weeks. Please feel free to adjust your pace according to the needs of your group. If the need arises to take a week and give attention to needs in your group, do so. Then come back to the study guide the next week. We encourage you to periodically meet together specifically for the purpose of building relationships within your group.

Purpose Driven Group Guidelines

It's a good idea for every group to put words to their shared values, expectations, and commitments. Such guidelines will help you avoid unspoken agendas and unmet expectations. We recommend you discuss your guidelines during Session One in order to lay the foundation for a healthy group experience. Feel free to modify anything that does not work for your group.

If the idea of a written agreement is unfamiliar to your group, we encourage you to give it a try.

We agree to the following values:

Clear Purpose	To grow healthy spiritual lives by building a healthy small group community
Group Attendance	To give priority to the group meeting (call if I am absent or late)
Safe Environment	To create a safe place where people can be heard and feel loved (no quick answers, snap judgments, or simple fixes)
Be Confidential	To keep anything that is shared strictly confidential and within the group
Conflict Resolution	To avoid gossip and to immediately resolve any concerns by following the principles of Matthew 18:15–17
Spiritual Health	To give group members permission to speak into my life and help me live a healthy, balanced spiritual life that is pleasing to God
Limit Our Freedom	To limit our freedom by not serving or consuming alcohol during small group meetings or events so as to avoid causing a weaker brother or sister to stumble (1 Corinthians 8:1–13; Romans 14:19–21)
Welcome Newcomers	To invite friends who might benefit from this study and warmly welcome newcomers
Building Relationships	To get to know the other members of the group and pray for them regularly
Other	_____
	_____
	_____

Purpose Driven Group Agreement

We have also discussed and agree on the following items:

Child Care

_____

_____

Starting Time

_____

Ending Time

_____

If you haven't already done so, take a few minutes to fill out the *Small Group Calendar* on page 71.

Circles of Life—Small Group Connections

Discover who you can connect in community

Use this chart to help carry out one of the values in the *Purpose Driven Group Guidelines* and *Purpose Driven Group Agreement*, to "Welcome Newcomers."

> *"Come follow me . . . and I will make you fishers of men."*
> Matthew 4:19 (NIV)

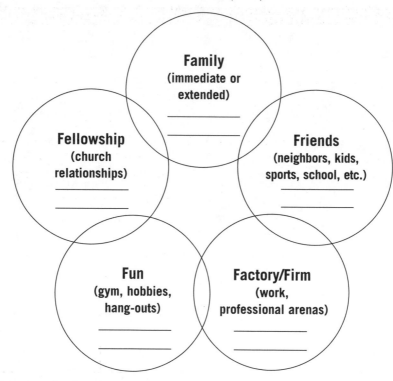

Follow this simple three-step process:

1. List one to two people in each circle.

2. Prayerfully select one person or couple from your list and tell your group about them.

3. Give them a call and invite them to your next meeting. Over fifty percent of those invited to a small group say, "Yes!"

Small Group Prayer and Praise Report

This is a place where you can write each other's requests for prayer. You can also make a note when God answers a prayer. Pray for each other's requests. If you're new to group prayer, it's okay to pray silently or to pray by using just one sentence: "God, please help

_____ to _____."

DATE	PERSON	PRAYER REQUEST	PRAISE REPORT

Small Group Prayer and Praise Report

DATE	PERSON	PRAYER REQUEST	PRAISE REPORT

Small Group Calendar

Healthy groups share responsibilities and group ownership. It might take some time for this to develop. Shared ownership ensures that responsibility for the group doesn't fall to one person. Use the calendar to keep track of social events, mission projects, birthdays, or days off. Complete this calendar at your first or second meeting. Planning ahead will increase attendance and shared ownership.

DATE	LESSON	LOCATION	FACILITATOR	SNACK OR MEAL
10/22	Session 2	Steve & Laura	Bill Jones	John & Alice

How the Assessment Works

The *Purpose Driven Health Assessment* is designed to help you evaluate how well you are balancing the five purposes in your life, and to identify your areas of strength and weakness. The Assessment consists of thirty-five statements that are linked to the five purposes.

Instructions

1. Rate yourself on each of the statements using a scale from 0 to 5, with zero meaning the statement does not match you and five meaning it is a very strong match for you.

2. After you have rated each statement, tally the results by transferring your ratings for each of the statements to the scoring table on this page. Then add up the numbers in each column to find your score for each purpose.

3. Turn to the *Purpose Driven Health Plan* on page 74 for further instructions.

My Spiritual Health Assessment

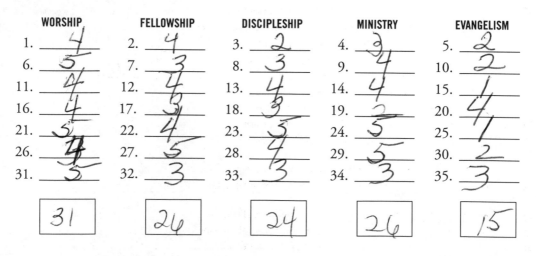

WORSHIP	FELLOWSHIP	DISCIPLESHIP	MINISTRY	EVANGELISM
1. 4	2. 4	3. 2	4. 3	5. 2
6. 5	7. 3	8. 3	9. 4	10. 2
11. 4	12. 4	13. 4	14. 4	15. 1
16. 4	17. 3	18. 3	19. 2	20. 4
21. 5	22. 4	23. 5	24. 5	25. 1
26. 4	27. 5	28. 4	29. 5	30. 2
31. 5	32. 3	33. 3	34. 3	35. 3
31	26	24	26	15

PURPOSE DRIVEN HEALTH ASSESSMENT

Spiritual Health Assessment

	Doesn't Match		Partial Match		Strong Match

1. Pleasing God with my life is my highest priority. … 0 1 2 3 4 5
2. I am genuinely open and honest about who I am with others. … 0 1 2 3 4 5
3. I quickly confess anything in my character that does not look like Christ. … 0 1 2 3 4 5
4. I often think about how to use my time more wisely to serve God. … 0 1 2 3 4 5
5. I feel personal responsibility to share my faith with those who don't know Jesus. … 0 1 2 3 4 5
6. I am dependent on God for every aspect of my life. … 0 1 2 3 4 5
7. I regularly use my time and resources to care for the needs of others. … 0 1 2 3 4 5
8. How I spend my time and money shows that I think more about God and others than I do about myself. … 0 1 2 3 4 5
9. I am currently serving God with the gifts and passions he has given me. … 0 1 2 3 4 5
10. I look for opportunities to build relationships with those who don't know Jesus. … 0 1 2 3 4 5
11. There is nothing in my life that I have not surrendered to (kept back from) God. … 0 1 2 3 4 5
12. I have a deep and meaningful connection with others in the church. … 0 1 2 3 4 5
13. I allow God's Word to guide my thoughts and change my actions. … 0 1 2 3 4 5
14. I regularly reflect on how my life can have an impact for the Kingdom of God. … 0 1 2 3 4 5
15. I regularly pray for those who don't know Christ. … 0 1 2 3 4 5
16. I regularly meditate on God's Word and invite him into my everyday activities. … 0 1 2 3 4 5
17. I have an easy time allowing someone who knows me to speak truth to me. … 0 1 2 3 4 5
18. I am able to praise God during difficult times and see them as opportunities to grow. … 0 1 2 3 4 5
19. I often think about ways to use my God-given SHAPE to please God. … 0 1 2 3 4 5
20. I am confident in my ability to share my faith. … 0 1 2 3 4 5
21. I have a deep desire to be in God's presence and spend time with him. … 0 1 2 3 4 5
22. I gather regularly with a group of Christians for fellowship and accountability. … 0 1 2 3 4 5
23. I find I am making more choices that cause me to grow when I am tempted to do wrong. … 0 1 2 3 4 5
24. I enjoy meeting the needs of others without expecting anything in return. … 0 1 2 3 4 5
25. My heart is full of passion to share the good news of the gospel with those who have never heard it. … 0 1 2 3 4 5
26. I am the same person at church that I am in private. … 0 1 2 3 4 5
27. There is nothing in my relationships that is currently unresolved. … 0 1 2 3 4 5
28. I have found that prayer has changed how I view and interact with the world. … 0 1 2 3 4 5
29. Those closest to me would say my life is a reflection of giving more than receiving. … 0 1 2 3 4 5
30. I find that my relationship with Jesus comes up frequently in my conversations with those who don't know him. … 0 1 2 3 4 5
31. I have an overwhelming sense of God's awesomeness even when I do not feel his presence. … 0 1 2 3 4 5
32. There is nothing in the way I talk or act concerning others that I would not be willing to share with them in person. … 0 1 2 3 4 5
33. I am consistent in pursuing habits that are helping me model my life after Jesus. … 0 1 2 3 4 5
34. I am open about my weaknesses and see them as opportunities to minister to others. … 0 1 2 3 4 5
35. I am open to going anywhere God calls me in whatever capacity to share my faith. … 0 1 2 3 4 5

Purpose Driven Health Plan

After completing the *Purpose Driven Health Assessment*, focus on the areas with lower scores or where you feel you need to plan for growth, and complete this *Purpose Driven Health Plan*. Fill in the possible ideas for developing your spiritual life in each area, then translate those possibilities into actual steps you plan to take to grow or develop in each purpose.

Possibilities	Plans (Strategic Steps)	
CONNECT (Fellowship) How can I deepen my relationships with others? • Family/friends • Relational/emotional development • Small group community		
GROW (Discipleship) How can I grow to be like Christ? • Spiritual disciplines • Financial stewardship • Character development		
SERVE (Ministry) How can I serve God and others? • Ministry to the Body • Leadership training • Continuing training		
SHARE (Evangelism) How can I share my faith regularly? • Mission to the world • Seeker friends/family, work, neighborhood involvement		
WORSHIP How can I live for God's pleasure? • Regular church attendance • Worship tapes and devotionals • Personal health and balance		

Answer Key

Session One: How to Profit from Your Problems

Problems are <u>inevitable</u>.

Problems are <u>unpredictable</u>.

Problems are <u>variable</u>.

Problems are <u>purposeful</u>.

Problems purify my <u>faith</u>.

Problems fortify my <u>patience</u>.

Problems sanctify my <u>character</u>.

God's Ultimate Purpose in my life: Building the <u>character of Christ</u> into my life.

<u>Rejoice</u>

We don't rejoice <u>for</u> the problem, but we rejoice <u>in</u> the problem.

<u>Pray</u>

Pray for <u>wisdom</u>.

<u>Relax</u>

Session Two: How to Make Up Your Mind

The Problem: <u>Indecision</u>

Unstable <u>emotions</u>

Unstable <u>relationships</u>

Unstable <u>spiritual life</u>

The Prescription: <u>Get Wisdom</u>

<u>Admit</u> my need.

Definition of Wisdom: Seeing life from God's <u>point of view</u>.

<u>Ask</u> for it.

<u>Anticipate</u> it.

The Promise: <u>God Will Give It</u>

<u>Continually</u>

<u>Generously</u>

<u>Without finding fault</u>

Session Three: How to Win over Temptation

Trials from <u>God</u>; designed to cause growth.

Temptations from <u>the devil</u>; designed to cause sin.

Be <u>realistic</u>.

Be <u>responsible</u>.

Be <u>ready</u>.

<u>Desire</u>

<u>Deception</u>

<u>Disobedience</u>

<u>Death</u>

Be <u>refocused</u>.

Be <u>reborn</u>.

<u>Fellowship</u> with other Christians.

Get into the <u>Word of God</u>.

Session Four: How to Be Blessed by the Bible

I must <u>receive</u> God's Word.

Be <u>careful</u>.

Be <u>calm</u>.

Be <u>clean</u>.

Be <u>compliant</u>.

I must <u>reflect</u> on God's Word.

<u>Read</u> it.

<u>Review</u> it.

<u>Remember</u> it.

I must <u>respond</u> to God's Word.

I must <u>practice</u> the Word.

<u>Controlled</u> mouth

<u>Caring</u> heart

<u>Clean</u> mind

Session Five: How to Treat People Right

<u>Appearance</u>

<u>Ancestry</u>

<u>Age</u>

<u>Achievement</u>

<u>Affluence</u>

Favoritism is <u>unchristian</u>.

Favoritism is <u>unreasonable</u>.

Favoritism is <u>unloving</u>.

<u>Accept</u> everybody.

<u>Appreciate</u> everybody.

<u>Affirm</u> everybody.

Session Six: How to Have Real Faith

PAUL

Fighting <u>legalism</u>

"Works" = Jewish <u>laws</u>

"Faith" = <u>root</u> of salvation

How to <u>know</u> you're a Christian

How to <u>become</u> a believer

JAMES

Fighting <u>laxity</u>

"Works" = Christian <u>lifestyle</u>

"Works" = <u>fruit</u> of salvation

How to <u>show</u> you're a Christian

How to <u>behave like</u> a believer

Real Faith is not just something you <u>say</u>.

Real Faith is not just something you <u>feel</u>.

Real Faith is not just something you <u>think</u>.

Real Faith is not just something you <u>believe</u>.

Real Faith is something you <u>do</u>.

Memory Verses

One of the most effective ways to deepen our understanding of the principles we are learning in this series is to memorize key Scripture verses. For many, Bible memorization is a new concept or one that has been difficult in the past. But we encourage you to stretch yourself and try to memorize these six *Memory Verses*. If possible, memorize them as a group and make them part of your group time.

I have hidden your word in my heart that I might not sin against you.
Psalm 119:11 (NIV)

Session One

Consider it pure joy, my brothers, whenever you face trials of many kinds, because you know that the testing of your faith develops perseverance.
James 1:2–3 (NIV)

Session Two

If any of you lacks wisdom, he should ask God, who gives generously to all without finding fault, and it will be given to him. But when he asks, he must believe and not doubt, because he who doubts is like a wave of the sea, blown and tossed by the wind.
James 1:5–6 (NIV)

Session Three

Blessed is the man who perseveres under trial, because when he has stood the test, he will receive the crown of life that God has promised to those who love him.
James 1:12 (NIV)

Session Four

But the man who looks intently into the perfect law that gives freedom and continues to do this, not forgetting what he has heard, but doing it—he will be blessed in what he does.
James 1:25 (NIV)

Session Five

If you really keep the royal law found in Scripture, "Love your neighbor as yourself," you are doing right. But if you show favoritism, you sin and are convicted by the law as lawbreakers.
James 2:8–9 (NIV)

Session Six

In the same way, faith by itself, if it is not accompanied by action, is dead.
James 2:17 (NIV)
